CRYSTAL MAZE MYSTERY
BOOK 2

THE CRYSTAL THIEF

In this *Crystal Maze Mystery*, you can share the adventures
of Sue, Baz and Jane as they travel through the
Time Zones in search of Marvo, the cunning crystal thief.
Tackle the puzzles, clues and coded messages which the
amazing trio encounter on their way through the Maze.
Try to solve each puzzle before turning the page. If you need
a little help, there are clues on pages 43 - 44 and if you're still
stuck on the hardest ones, you can look up the answers on
pages 45 - 48 before moving on to the next part of the story.

Keep your wits about you, and good luck, Crystal Mazers!

CRYSTAL MAZE MYSTERY

Book 2

THE CRYSTAL THIEF

Text by Peter Arnold

Illustrations by Mick Reid

Based on *The Crystal Maze* series.
A Chatsworth Television Production
for Channel Four.

MAMMOTH

First published in Great Britain 1993 by Mammoth
an imprint of Reed Consumer Books Ltd
Michelin House, 81 Fulham Road, London SW3 6RB
and Auckland, Melbourne, Singapore and Toronto

Reprinted 1993

ISBN 0 7497 1380 1

A CIP catalogue record for this title
is available from the British Library

Printed in Great Britain
by Scotprint Ltd. Musselburgh

STOLEN CRYSTALS!

Sue, Baz and Jane were waiting to watch an episode of their favourite TV series being filmed, when suddenly Richard O'Brien tore past. He turned and called out to them, 'The crystals have been stolen! Can you help me catch the thief?'

They didn't need persuading!

'Come on, then. Into the Maze!'

THE MYSTERIOUS MARVO

They found themselves in the Futuristic Zone. A corridor led them to a spaceship.

'Who's the thief?' asked Baz, when they'd sat down.

'His name's Marvo,' said Richard, 'but he'll be in disguise. Usually he is clean-shaven, eats a lot of sweets, and when he is travelling he always listens to his Walkman. But he cannot disguise his right hand because his middle finger is missing.'

After a while Sue said, 'I think I know who he is.'

Can you work out who Marvo is?

This is Captain Berk. We are leaving for Futura Distanka. Fasten your safety belts.

MARVO'S CLUES

When the spaceship landed, the captain told the passengers to leave row by row to catch the monorails to the city.

'We'll lose him,' Baz groaned.

'He's leaving some papers in the rack,' said Jane. When their turn came to leave, she picked them up. 'It's a map and a sort of code!'

'Mad Marvo has a wicked sense of humour,' said Richard. 'He will leave lots of clues, and enjoy us chasing him – but be careful. He'll make things difficult for us.'

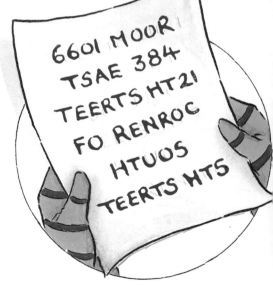

Can you decode the message? Where in the city must they go?

RIVER

MONORAIL STATION

SOUTH 5TH STREET

OVERHEAD MONORAIL

SOUTH 4TH STREET

SOUTH 3RD STREET

EAST 10TH

EAST 11TH

EAST 12TH

9

SMOKING PROBLEM

Room 1066 was unlocked. There was a crystal on the table and a strange word-game on the wall.

'It probably tells us what to do next,' said Richard.

Just then there was a click.

'We're locked in!' Sue gasped.

Suddenly, smoke began to fill the room.

'Quick!' spluttered Richard. 'We must solve the puzzle or we'll suffocate!'

Can you find the missing piece for the wall, and solve the word game?

THE KEY TO THE PROBLEM

They found the key and fell out of the door. Sue picked up a note. 'Roundabout where?' she asked.

Jane knew where to go – do you?

On a roundabout was another crystal, and pinned to it by a dart was a teddy bear.

What should they do next?

RICHARD IS LEFT BEHIND

Jane won the bear – after several attempts, for which Richard paid! Inside its arm were three train tickets.

'Quick,' urged Richard. 'Let's go.'

At the station, he ushered them into the waiting train, and rushed off to get himself a ticket. But the doors closed and the train pulled out just as he was running back.

'Oh no!' exclaimed Baz. 'Now we'll have to find Marvo on our own.'

'We don't even know what Marvo looks like without his disguise, or how far ahead he is,' Jane said glumly.

'Let's hope Richard can catch up with us later,' said Sue.

They got out at the Aztec Zone.

'A gentleman said you left this briefcase behind,' said a porter.

The case had MARVO printed on it, so Jane took it.

Meanwhile Baz was looking through the station exit. 'There's only one path,' he said. 'It goes through a wood. I suppose we'd better follow it.'

Why did Richard miss the train? Is Marvo ahead of them or not?

SUE'S PERILOUS CLIMB

Inside the briefcase were three pieces of paper and a crystal. 'We'll keep these for later,' said Sue, as they followed the path through the wood towards a mountain. Suddenly they were surrounded by a group of hostile villagers who tied them to stakes in front of a huge idol.

'On the mountain is a red flower whose bloom belongs to our god,' said the chief. 'But the paths up are guarded by poisonous snakes. If you want your freedom one of you must fetch it.' Sue volunteered to go.

Can you see a safe path up?

THE MISSING BLOOM

Sue searched for the flower but it had gone, and in its place was a crystal. She knew Marvo was the culprit, and that without the bloom they were lost.

Where could Marvo have gone?

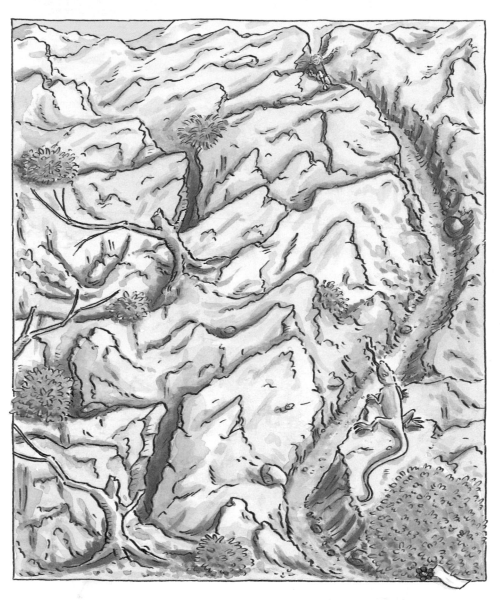

Through a gap in the rocks Sue saw a path leading downhill. She could see the picked red bloom at the end of the path, with what looked like a note. But in the way was a giant iguana! She was desperate. She had to find another way down to the bloom.

Can you see another way down, avoiding the path and iguana?

TRAPPED IN THE TEMPLE

By using the trees to help her get across cracks in the rock, Sue managed to collect the bloom and the note and get back. She found the way down the mountain and delivered the flower. Their delighted captors released Jane and Baz and took them back to their village for a drink of berry juice.

Sue showed Baz and Jane the note. 'It's a sort of cipher, ' she said. 'It should tell us what to do next.'

Jane deciphered the note – can you?

Inside the temple a heavy door led to a catacomb of tunnels. Suddenly they heard the turn of a key and a maniacal laugh. 'We're trapped!' said Sue. 'We must find another way out.' Tearing through the tunnels, they finally reached another door.

Reading the sign, Jane asked anxiously, 'Whose age shall we use?'
'Mine,' said Baz. 'But hurry!'

Do you know which key opens the door?

THIS IS THE KEY

FROM YOUR AGE TAKE AWAY FOUR MULTIPLY BY TEN AND THEN TAKE AWAY YOUR AGE AND ADD FORTY MORE DIVIDE BY YOUR AGE AND OPEN THE DOOR

BAZ THE BRAVE

They found the right key and went through the door. On the other side they met a fortune-teller who led them to her den.

'One of you must volunteer to answer my question,' said the fortune-teller. 'Get it right and I will give all three of you the means to follow Marvo. But get it wrong and whoever answers must remain here with me. It's the rule, I'm afraid.'

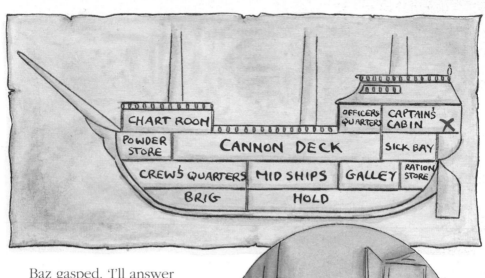

Baz gasped. 'I'll answer the question,' he said.

'Tell me, then,' said the fortune-teller. 'If you give a GORILLA an AT, what other dangerous beast can you make?'

Baz thought hard while Sue and Jane looked on anxiously. Finally he worked out the answer. 'Well done, my dearies,' said the kindly fortune-teller, while Sue and Jane tried to look as if they always knew Baz would answer correctly.

'Marvo has gone to the Ocean Zone,' the fortune-teller said. 'Take these air cylinders, face masks and flippers. The end of this passage overlooks a bay. This plan is of a sunken ship wrecked there. The X shows where the crystals are. They are in a chest – here is the key. You must find it quickly because the air in the cylinders gives you just ten minutes to surface by the island in the centre of the bay. Good luck.'

Would you have solved the fortune-teller's riddle?

23

THE WRECK

Sure enough, at the end of the passage they came to a huge bay with an island in the centre. They dived in and, as the weeds thinned out, saw the wonderful sight of a sunken ship.

Where is the chest?

BOATING BUSINESS

Inside the chest was a small bag. Back on the island, they opened it, to find only stones and a tiny totem pole.

'There must be a totem pole here,' said Jane. And there was – but as

Sue reached for the note attached to it, she fell into a deep pit.

'We must leave Sue here for now,' said Jane, when she'd understood the note. 'We must take a boat west – towards the setting sun.'

FROM THE HUT 1, 3, 6, 10, 11

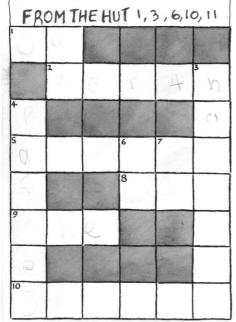

They came to a shore on which stood a fisherman's hut. There they found a crystal and a rope ladder, with which they returned and got Sue out of the pit. She was holding a box.

'It's a *Crystal Maze* crossword game,' she said. 'The words fit on to the grid so that each space, across and down, is a complete word.'

'Let's solve it in the hut,' said Jane. 'We can stay the night there.'

Can you make sense of the note on the totem pole?
Can you solve the crossword game?
In which direction should they now go?

A DODGY CROSSING

Next morning, the three friends started walking north. They came to a large river, with stepping stones across.

'We have to work out which stones to walk on,' said Sue, reading the board.

'What do the pictures mean?' asked Baz.

Can you work out the safe route?

THE RIDDLE OF THE STONES
Some stones are true
Some stones are false
Those who chose true
reached the bank.
Those who chose false
found they sank
and became supper
for the alligators.
Proceed traveller to the other end.
Allow confidence to be your friend

They worked out the riddle, and, treading carefully, they reached the opposite bank.

'I know where to go now!' Jane announced, excitedly.

Which direction should they take, and why?

On the note:

Haha,
Marvo leads you
a merry dance.
Through the falls
are dancers
who do NOT
hold the answer.

BAZ'S SALAD

With no sign of a clue at the waterfall, Sue remembered an old message, which they decoded.

Baz dived into the water. He found the crystal, but it was tied to a sack, buried in pebbles.

Inside, were fruit and vegetables of many colours. There was a red strawberry, a yellow lemon, an orange carrot, a brown onion, a green lettuce and a plum, which can only be called plum-coloured.

'What must we do next, make a blooming salad?' grumbled Baz.

'No,' said Jane. 'There's also another instruction from Marvo here. Let's go behind the waterfall, and maybe things will become clearer then.'

Which old message did Sue remember? What did it say?

YE PLUM TREE INN

BEARDED LADY

32

A SUPER MARKET

Behind the waterfall was a cave, at the other end of which they were confronted by an incredible scene.

'The Medieval Zone!' said Sue. 'It's market day. I suppose Marvo's message and the items he hid tell us where to go next.'

Where do you think they should go?

LOCKED IN!

At Ye Plum Tree Inn, the landlord sent them up to Room 4. Marvo had left a game, some cakes, and three goblets of lemonade.

'I don't drink lemonade,' grumbled Jane. 'And the game's difficult because some pictures can pair up with two of the others.'

Try to pair the pictures correctly and find their next destination.

'I know the windmills,' said Baz. They searched them all without success. Then suddenly Sue and Baz collapsed on some straw in the ruined windmill next to the one with sails. Jane couldn't wake them. 'They've been drugged!' she thought.

Just then, she heard someone coming, and hid behind a bush. It was Marvo! He locked Sue and Baz in, threw the key away, and hurried off, muttering, 'Where's the other one?'

'So *that's* Marvo,' Jane said to herself. 'I must rescue Sue and Baz!' She went back to the village to get help.

How do you think Sue and Baz were drugged?

35

RICK RETURNS!

As Jane was asking a young villager if he had any rope, another villager standing nearby offered to help. He led her to an old shed but then he pushed her through the door and locked it. Jane heard a maniacal laugh. Marvo again!

Jane could do nothing, so she lay down and dozed off.

Suddenly the door caved in, and standing there was Richard O'Brien with the young villager.

'It's resourceful Rick, rushing to the rescue,' said Richard. 'Where are the others?'

Jane related to Richard all their adventures since they had lost him at the railway station, and explained that Sue and Baz were now trapped in the ruined windmill.

'Then let's go!' said Richard and, thanking the villager for leading him to Jane, they set off.

Jane told Richard that Sue and Baz were in the mill next to the one with the sails, and outlined her plan to rescue them by tying the rope to the tree, and using the rail which ran round the edge of the sails of the windmill.

'I was relying on a villager to help,' she said to Richard, 'but your arrival solves everything.'

Can you guess Jane's complicated plan to rescue Sue and Baz?

POETRY POSER

When Baz and Sue had been rescued, the four Mazers returned to the village, knowing they were close behind Marvo.

'We'll start looking for him at Ye Plum Tree Inn,' said Richard. But, as they arrived at the village, Jane, who knew what Marvo looked like without his disguise since she had seen him by the windmills, suddenly noticed him running towards a horse.

'There he is,' she cried, but Marvo leapt on the horse and galloped off. As he did so, he dropped a bag.

'Let him go,' said Richard. 'At least we've got the crystals.'

But they were tricked again! When they opened the bag, it was full of papers – and one solitary crystal.

'I don't believe it,' groaned Baz.

'You don't seem too worried,' Sue said to Richard as he played a tune on his mouth organ. 'Look! Most of these papers are 'Wanted' leaflets with Marvo's face on them. But this one is different. There are strange rhymes dotted all over the page.'

'Read them out,' said Baz. 'Let's see if we can make sense of them.'

Sue read out the little poems to the accompaniment of Richard's music. Some of the villagers thought they were putting on an entertainment, and one of them even clapped!

'I think I can see what some of the rhymes mean,' said Jane, 'but I'm not sure how it helps us.'

They all examined the strange piece of paper. At last light dawned for Baz.

'I think I understand,' he said. 'Come with me. If I'm right perhaps this will lead us to the crystals at last!'

Can you work out the meaning of the mysterious poems, and where the crystals might be?

THE CRYSTAL DOME

They wound up the bucket from the well. It was full of crystals! 'Are they all there?' Richard asked. 'How many did you collect while chasing Marvo?'

'Seven,' Sue said.

'That's thirty-five seconds in the Crystal Dome,' laughed Jane.

'You're right,' replied Richard. 'Come with me.'

He led them into a dark barn, through a door, along a corridor, and there was the Crystal Dome.

'OK,' said Richard. 'When I blow the whistle, collect as many gold tokens as you can. Stop at the second whistle. At the end, any silver tokens are taken away from the gold tokens. Ready?'

As he blew his whistle, the tokens fluttered into the air.

When the three emerged from the Dome, Richard said, 'Among your gold tokens are seven words. Among your silver tokens are seven letters. Take silver from gold and you have a last mystery message from Marvo.'

Try to work out what the message is.

MARVO UNMASKED

At last, Sue, Jane and Baz watched their favourite programme being made. Richard introduced them to all the people involved in the show: Mumsie, Ralph, the director, camera crew etc.

Suddenly Sue looked agitated. 'I know who Marvo is . . . it's Ralph!'

'Sssh, I know,' whispered Richard. 'But keep it quiet. Poor Ralph gets so fed up that he doesn't run the show himself that sometimes he changes his personality – Mad Marvo is just one of his disguises. We put up with him because he is an old friend of Mumsie's. Don't worry – I have a nice little punishment lined up for him later.'

Jane, Baz and Sue did not tell anybody about Mad Marvo, but whenever they watched *The Crystal Maze*, they smiled at their behind-the-scenes secret.

Can you spot Ralph/Marvo in the picture?

CLUES

PAGES 6-7
You can rule out all the women, all the men who are not listening to Walkmans, and all the men who you can see have not got a finger missing on their right hands. Is there anybody left?

PAGES 8-9
The code relates to a place in the city. See if you can work out where it is.

PAGES 10-11
Will any board fit in to make sense of the top line?

PAGE 12
What might Jane have noticed as she left the monorail station?

PAGE 13
Have a look round the fair. Is the dart a clue?

PAGES 14-15
Is there something fishy going on which might delay Richard? Which train might Marvo have caught?

PAGE 18
Is there anything in the landscape which suggests somebody might have passed by?

PAGE 19
Are there things Sue could cling to, to help her reach the bloom?

PAGE 20
Try one of the pieces of paper found in the briefcase handed to the crystal-seekers by the monorail porter.

PAGE 21
Instead of guessing Baz's age, try using your own to work out the sum.

Page 22
Can you use the letters of GORILLA and AT to make something you wouldn't like to meet in water?

PAGES 26-27
a) Will the note fit another mysterious note to make sense?
b) In the crossword game, don't forget some down words are joined to across words and vice versa.
c) If you solve the crossword you can work out the direction to take if you remember Baz and Jane's journey from the island.

PAGES 28-29

a) How can confidence be your friend and help in crossing the stones? What letters do the objects drawn on the stones begin with?

b) On the far bank, how do you think they can follow in Marvo's footsteps?

PAGES 30-31

a) Did Sue remember an earlier unused message?

b) Suppose the message is signed 'Marvo'. Does this suggest a relation between the numbers and the 26 letters of the alphabet?

PAGES 32-33

Remember Marvo's message about dancers? What are they holding? Can these be matched with the items in the sack? What are they *not* holding? Does this suggest somewhere in the scene?

PAGE 34

Translate the pictures into words, then put one word in front of another until two words seem to make a pair. Try to get six pairs, and select the one with i's.

PAGE 35

What do you know of the recent eating and drinking activity of Baz, Sue and Jane?

PAGE 37

Jane must get one end of the rope through the open roof of the windmill where Sue and Baz are sleeping. Don't forget that Sue and Baz must get down from the top of the windmill.

PAGE 39

Could the poems relate to things around the village?

PAGE 41

Some of the letters appear in only one of the words, so you can take these letters away and make new words. When you have seven new words, put them in order to make an appropriate message.

PAGE 42

What do you think is the oddest thing about Marvo which might help you to spot him?

ANSWERS

PAGES 6-7

Marvo is the person ringed. He is wearing a false beard, and gloves, so you can't see the missing finger. He is listening to his Walkman, but not eating sweets (Richard didn't say he ate sweets *all* the time).

PAGES 8-9

When read backwards, the coded message reads:
ROOM 1066, 483 EAST 12th STREET
CORNER OF SOUTH 5th STREET
It means Marvo's pursuers must go to this address in the city. The map indicates which block the message refers to.

PAGES 10-11

The word game is completed thus:
SUN   RISE = DAY   BREAK
Key is: UNDER TABLE   Get going!
It tells the crystal-chasers to look under the table.

PAGE 12

When leaving the monorail station Jane had seen the fair in the park, and knew that somewhere in the fair there would be a roundabout.

PAGE 13

They should go to the dart-throwing stall, and try to win the large teddy – the bear pinned to the roundabout horse is a copy of it.

PAGES 14-15

Marvo deliberately delayed Richard by sending him the wrong way for tickets. Marvo is travelling in the same train as Sue, Baz and Jane.

PAGES 16-17

The route from bottom to top of the mountain is marked.

PAGE 18

Marvo has gone through a gap in the ridge. On the prickly bush is a piece of cloth torn from his trousers.

PAGE 19

By holding on to bushes and branches, this is the route Sue follows:

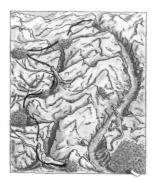

PAGE 20

The key was on the torn piece of paper in the briefcase the monorail porter gave the crystal-seekers. Although the key is incomplete, the symbols are obviously in groups of three, so the symbol for the letters H, I, N, O, T and U can easily be worked out. This leaves only a few blanks, and when the rest of the letters are written down, the missing letters become obvious. All that is left is to divide the message up into words. It reads:
I HAVE HIDDEN THE CRYSTALS IN THE CRYPT BELOW THE TEMPLE

PAGE 21

Key number 9 opens the door. It doesn't matter whose age you use in the sum, the answer is always 9. As it happens, Baz is 9. Take away 4 leaves 5. Multiply by 10 makes 50. Take away 9 leaves 41. Add 40 more makes 81. Divide by 9 gives 9.

PAGE 23

The letters GORILLA and AT can be rearranged to make ALLIGATOR.

PAGES 24-25

The place where the chest is is circled.

PAGES 26-27

a) The note joins the one found in the briefcase handed to the children by the porter at the monorail station, and which Baz has been carrying in his bag (see page 16). The two halves joined give this message:

Hee hee, what a Marvo-lous joke!
Take a boat west to a hut
where there's a rope-ladder. Return
before nightfall – if the victim
sleeps the vampire bats will strike!
b) The completed crossword looks like this:

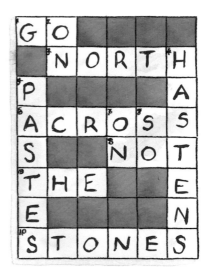

The message at the bottom, when the answers are substituted for the words numbered 1,3,6,10,11 is:

FROM THE HUT, GO NORTH ACROSS THE STONES

c) From the hut the three know that the island in the lake is due east (because they had to row west to get from the island to the hut). So if they know east, it is easy to work out north.

PAGES 28-29

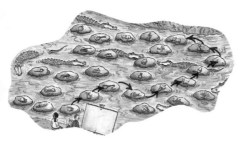

a) The word CONFIDENCE is the key to crossing the stones. The true path is on the stones with pictures beginning with those letters. The path across is: Cup, Owl, Noose, Fish, Ice cream, Dog, Egg, Nose, Cat, Elephant.
b) Marvo's footprints can be seen going in the direction of the waterfall. Jane recognizes them from when they were on the island (page 26).

PAGES 30-31
a) Sue remembered the third piece of paper in the briefcase handed them by the monorail porter (see page 16).
b) The code is simple. Each letter represents a number, but the numbers start at Z for number 1 and work backwards:

A	B	C	D	E	F	G	H	I	J
26	25	24	23	22	21	20	19	18	17

K	L	M	N	O	P	Q	R	S	T
16	15	14	13	12	11	10	9	8	7

U	V	W	X	Y	Z
6	5	4	3	2	1

The message therefore reads:
A CRYSTAL LIES AT THE FOOT OF THE FALLS MARVO

PAGES 32-33
Marvo's message clearly relates to the Morris Dancers, who are holding ribbons of five colours. These colours can be matched to five of the items in Marvo's sack: orange = carrot; yellow = lemon; red = strawberry; green = lettuce; brown = onion. The item left over is the plum. The dancers are *not* holding a plum-coloured ribbon. The plum is therefore the clue, and the place the children must go is Ye Plum Tree Inn. If you look closely you will even see Marvo's face peering round a curtain there.

PAGE 34
The pictures on the tiles pair up as follows: Foxglove (a flower), windmill, key ring, car boot, ear drum and bookcase. Windmill is the one with two 'i's, so the three adventurers have to find a windmill.

PAGE 35
The drug which made Baz and Sue drowsy was in the lemonade provided by Marvo. Jane said she didn't drink it, and didn't touch her glass, so avoided the drug.

Richard and Jane tie one end of the rope to the tree. Jane climbs on to the sail of the windmill while Richard gets the rope round the other sail so that he can pull it into a vertical position. Jane's sail is now horizontal, and Jane is near the top of the mill that Sue and Baz are in. Richard then releases the rope from his sail, and throws the end up to Jane on the other sail. She passes the end through the rail on her sail and reels in enough rope to throw through the open top of the windmill for it to reach Sue and Baz. With the rope taut from the tree, Sue can climb up the inside of the windmill. She can then swing to the ground on the rope while it is held aloft by the sail on which Jane is sitting. The sail will drop, of course (Jane must hold on), but it will slow the fall from 15 feet enough for Sue's fall to be gentle. The process is then repeated to get Baz down.

PAGE 39

The poems constitute a map of the village. They refer to: the bearded lady (whose chin you can't see), the ducks (whose feet you can't see), the boxers (whose fists you can't see), the Morris Dancers (coloured hose), the sheep (who could end in a stew), the horses (who only say 'neigh'), the knife grinder (as sharp as me). This leaves 'the prize to dazzle the eyes', which must be the crystals. If you look at

the village on pages 32-33, you will see this poem is in the position where the well is. The crystals are down the well!

PAGE 41

Take B from BRICK, G from FANGS, I from MAIZE, J from JAM, S from IS, C from WITCH and W from WHERE.
The seven new words can be rearranged to make the message:

MAZE FANS I AM HERE WITH RICK

PAGE 42

Marvo/Ralph is the man in the yellow shirt. You can see his right hand has the middle finger missing.